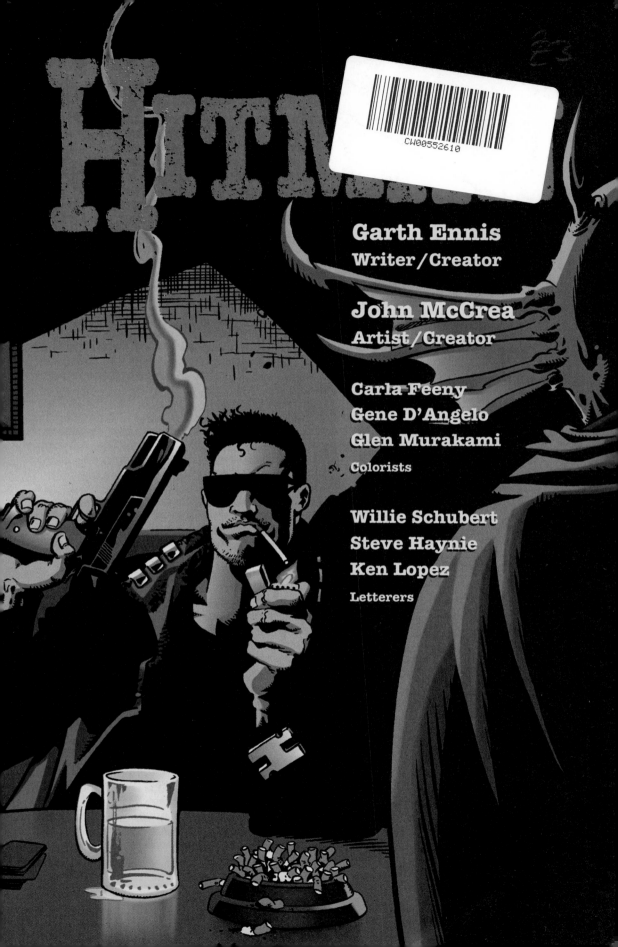

HITMAN

Garth Ennis
Writer/Creator

John McCrea
Artist/Creator

Carla Feeny
Gene D'Angelo
Glen Murakami
Colorists

Willie Schubert
Steve Haynie
Ken Lopez
Letterers

INTRODUCTION

How's this for a plan? Come up with an idea for a crossover series that creates a swarm of new heroes and villains, haul them up a flagpole and see which one gets saluted. That, in essence, was the thinking behind DC's BLOODLINES and, in my cynical opinion, it was worth it for one reason — HITMAN. I threw a pretty snappy salute in the direction of Tommy Monaghan when I first made his acquaintance, and I'm glad to see that I wasn't alone in thinking that he deserved more than the odd cameo role. The man's a star — and he knows it.

Garth Ennis and John McCrea, a couple of decent blokes from Belfast, have come up with something a bit different in HITMAN. There are quite a few British and Irish creators plying their trade in the American comic-book industry, but you tend to find them skulking about in DC's VERTIGO titles where they can have their wicked way with the "mature readers" market. Recently, a few editors have been foolish enough to unleash some of us perverse island people on the mainstream super-hero universe, and Garth and John have used this opportunity to present us with their own distinct view of Gotham City and its citizenry.

One such citizen is the above-mentioned Tommy Monaghan, a man who gained some good, old-fashioned super-powers (X-ray vision and telepathy) and didn't head straight for the Spandex shop with the idea of rushing out to save the world.

Tommy is a killer, a hitman who specializes in whacking his super-powered brethren and, between contracts, he likes nothing more than a session on the booze and a game of poker with some of his low-life friends. The thing that stops Tommy from attaining "really nasty piece of work" status is his determination not to off anyone he regards as one of the good guys.

This gray area between good and evil has become one of Garth's favorite stomping grounds, and there are very few writers in comics who can match him when it comes to breathing life into the characters who people the shadow world and deal with the conflicts between friendship and survival. John McCrea's art is perfect for this style of story. He can handle the humor, drama and action with equal proficiency and just the right amount of flair. Garth's scripts demand a lot of "acting" ability from the artists who work on them (an appreciation of the importance of facial expression and body language is vital if you are to bring a comic-book character to life) and, as you will see, John is no slouch in this department.

Garth and John have been partners in crime since the beginning of their professional careers. Those years together have given them an understanding of each other's work that helps make any collaboration between them a bit special and, because of that, the success of HITMAN comes as no surprise to me.

Cheers,
Steve Dillon

AT THE BACK OF HIS MIND...

PAST TWO MILLENNIA OF TREACHERY AND BLOODY DEATH, OF STUNTED LOVE AND FLOWERING HATE...

WAY DOWN IN THE DARK, THERE IS A PRISON.

HITMAN

CHAPTER ONE: BIRTH PAINS

GARTH ENNIS: SCRIPT
JOHN McCREA: ART
STEVE HAYNIE: LETTERS
GENE D'ANGELO: COLORS
PETER TOMASI: EDIT ASSISTS
DAN RASPLER: EDITS
THE DEMON CREATED BY JACK KIRBY
HITMAN CREATED BY ENNIS & McCREA

MIDNIGHT IN GOTHAM--

IT'S BARELY TWO YEARS SINCE, I WANDERED AWAY... WITH THE LOCAL BATTALION, OF THE OLD I.R.A....

THEY TOLD ME OF HEROES, I WANTED THE SAME... TO PLAY A GREAT PART IN...

THE PATRIOT GAME...

OH HO.

LET'S GO TO WORK.

6

I WANNA WAKE UP NOW! I WANNA WAKE UP!!

THERE'S NO PLACE LIKE HOME! THERE'S NO PLACE LIKE--

SHUK!

AAAK--!!

CHAPTER TWO:
FIRST BLOOD

PATIENCE, LITTLE ONE... PATIENCE...

THERE, THERE... IS THE JUICE OF THESE HUMANS NOT ENOUGH? DON'T WORRY...

I WILL GIVE YOU SOMETHING... *SPECIAL*...

MEEEEWWW... MEEEEWWW...

WHAT ARE YOU *DOING*, LISSIK?

I WAS GOING TO FEED HIM WITH THE FLESH OF OUR DEAD BROTHER SLODD, PRITOR...

NO!

THE TIME IS NOT YET RIGHT.

SOON, THOUGH... I CAN FEEL IT BUILDING INSIDE ME, *UNCOILING*...

YES, MY LORD...

AH... OUR FEEDING ON THE HUMANS... THEY TASTE GOOD, I KNOW, AND GIVE THE LITTLE ONE THE NUTRIENTS HE NEEDS...

BUT MORE AND MORE, THEY SURVIVE OUR ATTACKS-- AND GROW *MIGHTY*. SHOULD WE NOT ACT TO COUNTER THIS THREAT?

THREAT--? DON'T BE RIDICULOUS!

NOW, WHERE ARE THE OTHERS?

VENEV AND ANGON ARRIVED THIS MORNING. GEMIR IS ON HIS WAY... AH...

GLONTH HAS NOT YET LEFT GOTHAM CITY, LORD PRITOR. HE SAYS HE'S *STILL HUNGRY*...

GLONTH?!

"I SHOULD'VE *KNOWN* HE WOULD BE TROUBLE!"

HOPE MAGGIE CAN MAKE IT OUT TONIGHT...

BORRRRNNN INNA U.S.A., I WAS...

WONDER WHY THE COPS WANT THIS GUY?

UHHH...

HE'S WAKING UP--

BIG DEAL. YEAH, IF SHE COULD WEAR THAT WHITE DRESS...

BORRRNNN INNA U.S.A....

WHAT IS HE, A MOBSTER? WEIRD HOLE IN HIS NECK...

BETTER CALM HIM DOWN--

RELAX, MISTER. YOU'RE IN A HOSPITAL. YOU'LL BE FINE.

THE STRAPLESS, LOW-CUT ONE... HEH, HEH...

DUM, DUMDA-DUMDUMDUM...

HUH? JESUS, HIS EYES--

OH GREAT, A NUT. 'COS WHEN SHE LEANS FORWARD...

DUNNO THE WORDS... UHH... IIII WILL ALWAYS LOVE YOOOUU...

WHAT... WHO'S TALKIN'? WHO'S SAYIN' ALL THAT?

GOD, IT HURTS! I CAN HEAR-- WHAT'S--

UH-OH. ACID? SMACK? PLEASE NOT P.C.P....

NOW-- JUST RELAX, OKAY? EASY--!

LIKE MELONS--AW, JEEZ! COME ON, PAL, I LIKE AN EASY LIFE...

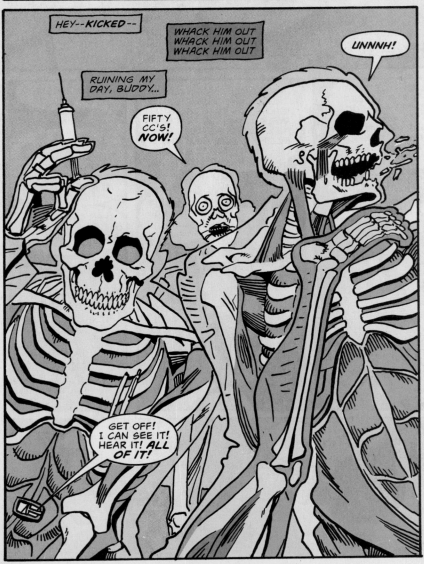

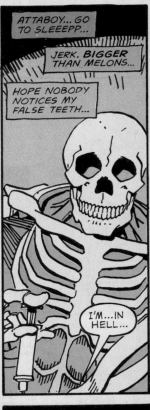

SOMEBODY'S GONNA *PAY* FOR THIS...

OUR OWN DEAR POP-- *SLAUGHTERED!* WHAT IN HELL COULDA *DONE* IT?

HEY! *BOSSES!*

JUST GOT WORD-- SEE THAT ROOM ACROSS THE STREET, THE WAY IT'S TRASHED, TOO?

COPS FOUND *TOMMY MONAGHAN* IN THERE, SAME STATE AS YOUR POP-- 'CEPT HE'S *STILL ALIVE!*

MONAGHAN? THE *HITMAN?*

THAT'S HIM! I GOT A GUY IN THE 4TH PRECINCT FEEDS ME INFO-- SAYS THEY FOUND A *RIFLE* IN THERE WITH HIM! THEY RECKON HE WOULDA *BLOWN YOUR POP AWAY* IF-- WHATEVER IT WAS-- HADN'T GOT HIM!

OH YEAH...? WHERE'S MONAGHAN NOW?

GOTHAM GENERAL, BOSSES.

'KAY. I FIGURE THOSE *BROOKLYN* PUNKS WANTED POP WHACKED AFTER THAT *ARMS DEAL*... I WANT MONAGHAN'S HEAD, GOT ME?

THEN I WANT LINES OUT ON WHATEVER S.O.B. DID THIS TO POP!

NOW *GET TO IT!*

YESSIRS!

YOU GOT IT, BOSSES!

UH... CAN YOU... CAN YOU HELP ME...?

RAN STRAIGHT INTO HER DAMN COOKIN' POT, IS MORE LIKE IT--AW, WHAT DOES THIS CREEP WANT?

HUH?

"MOM'S OWN RECIPE" MY BIG OL' BUTT --

WHAT'S THE MATTER?

GOT SOMETHIN' FOR YOU.

NO ONE MESSES WITH A GUY IN A COP'S UNIFORM. I'M CLEAR ACROSS TOWN BEFORE THEY KNOW IT.

AN' I'M STARTIN' TO THINK ABOUT THE THING THAT DID THIS TO ME...

LIFE USED TO BE SIMPLE. WHACK THE TARGET, TAKE THE DOUGH, LIVE A LITTLE. AN' NOW SPOOKY HAS TO SCREW IT ALL UP FOR ME...

WELL, SPOOKY...

YEAH, YEAH! I'M COMIN'!

TWO CAN PLAY AT THAT GAME.

MY GOD! IT WASN'T ME, OFFICER--

UH...

TOMMY?

HI, PAT.

JAAAASON! HELLOOOO!

REGGIE.

COOL AS ICE, AS EVER! DOOO COME IN!

THANK YOU SOOO MUCH FOR COMING TO MY TAAASTING...

LET ME START YOU WITH THIS LITTLE FELLOW-- AN '83 CABERNET FROM RAIMAT. FRUITY, FULL FLAVORED -- YOU CAN TASTE BLAAACKBERRIES IN IT, I'M SUUURE!

THANK YOU.

AND HOW ARE GLENDA AND RANDU?

MM--GLENDA IS WELL, THANK YOU. RANDU HAS SEEN BETTER DAYS, BUT HE SOLDIERS ON...

OH, JAAASON! YOU IMP!

KRUNCH!

EH?

SQUEEESHH!

EEEIIGHH!

KRESH!

NOW *YOU*, CASUAL ONE!

HHNNNG!

SKLUTCH!

GLAAARRHH!

YOU LITTLE WORM! I'LL SUCK YOUR HEART OUT!

WHAT? GONE OH FORM OF *WHAT*?

WHO'S "DIMMINY TRIGGIN"?

WHAMMM!

NNNNNGG!

BY MY DEAREST BROTHER GOAT--WHO'D'VE THOUGHT THE OAF WOULD FLOAT? DOWN THAT SEWER ALL SO DANK AND DIMLY LIT?

BUT JUST WATCH THE FELLOW FLURRY, THROUGH THAT MASS OF NOXIOUS SLURRY...

AAAAACHH--SHPTOO!

BAGELS 'R' US

HE REALLY SEEMS AT HOME IN ALL THAT--

FREEZE!

HA HA HA HA HA HA HA HA HA HA HA HA HA HA HA HA HA HA

WHOOOMPF

I GOT ALL THEM CLOTHES YA ASKED ME FOR, TOMMY. INNA BEDROOM...

GOOD.

YOU, AH... YOU GET ALL THIS STUFF FROM THE WAREHOUSE?

HECKLER AND KOCH

YEP. GUARDS NEVER EVEN SAW WHAT HIT 'EM.

I APPRECIATE YOU LETTIN' ME USE YOUR APARTMENT, PAT. I'LL GET THIS GEAR OUT OF HERE SOON AS I FIND A PLACE OF MY OWN.

UH...

AH, NO PROB, TOMMY. I AIN'T WORRIED.

YES YOU ARE. I *KNOW* YOU ARE.

AND IT AIN'T *TOMMY* ANYMORE, PAT.

CHAPTER THREE: FUNERAL FOR A FIEND

ROBERT HEAVINGTON DUBELZ WAS NOT A VERY NICE MAN.

HE LIED AND CHEATED AND STOLE AND MURDERED UNTIL HE HAD QUITE A NIFTY LITTLE CRIMINAL EMPIRE AT HIS DISPOSAL: GAMBLING, EXTORTION, NARCOTICS, PROSTITUTION-- ALL THE OLD FAVORITES...

BAD AS HE WAS, HE WAS NEVER AS BAD AS HIS SONS...

I TELLYA, WHEN WE GET THIS PUNK, HE'S MEAT!

YEAH. FOR YOU, POP. FOR THE SAKE OF YER MEMORY, WE GONNA HAVE THE SCUM DROWNED IN A DISHWASHER.

WHATSA NEWS, BOYS?

THAT'S SICK! STRAIGHT AFTER POP'S WAKE, WE GOTTA GO NAIL 'EM!

DAMN RIGHT! AN' YOU BOYS MAKE SURE YA COME TA THE WAKE, OR WE'RE COMIN' AFTER YA WITH A CHAINSAW SUPPOSITORY!

MONAGHAN'S STILL MISSING, BOSSES. THE SCARLOTTIS DOWN IN BROOKLYN HIRED HIM, LIKE YOU FIGURED-- THEY'RE MEAT AS OF TODAY.

AS FOR THE CREEP THAT KILLED YOUR POP-- LOOKS LIKE ONE OF THESE PARASITES THE SUPERJERKS BEEN FIGHTIN'. IT TOOK HIS SPINAL FLUID.

MOE AND JOE DUBELZ ARE TOTAL BASTARDS...

WAY I FIGURE IT, DUBELZ'S BOYS ARE GONNA BE AFTER ME FOR TRYIN' TO WASTE THEIR POP. SO, 'FORE I GO AFTER SPOOKY, I BETTER SCRATCH 'EM...

COUPLE OF THE HIRED SCUM USUALLY DRINK HERE.

NAN'S SLEAZY BAR

NOONAN'S

PITCHER OF BUD.

COMIN' UP.

LET'S SEE WHAT MEATHEAD'S THINKIN' ABOUT...

OLD MAN DUBELZ'S **WAKE** TOMORROW... HMMM... 'BOUT TIME I HAD A **RAISE**...

AH, THE WAKE. THAT'LL BE UP AT THE MANSION THE CREEPS'VE GOT...

GOOD A PLACE FOR A HIT AS ANY.

I'LL ASK THE BOSSES NEXT WEEK... HEY, BEER'S HERE...

SEVEN BUCKS.

RIGHT.

'NOTHER JACK, SEAN.

SURE.

MONAGHAN'S VOICE!

MONAGHAN!

HARD TO AVOID SOMETIMES, SEAN.

TELL ME ABOUT IT.

HADDA ICE A GUY ONCE FOR WINKIN' AT MY OLD LADY. TURNED OUT THE POOR SUCKER HAD A *TWITCH*...

'LEAST YOU GOT A GOOD STORY OUT OF IT.

'SCUSE ME A SECOND...

OKAY YOU SONS OF--

BLAM

YOU DIDN'T SEE ME, RIGHT?

WELL, I DID...

BUT YOU HAD A MASK ON. AN' YOU ORDERED CAPPUCCINO.

SEE YA, TOMMY.

HALF OF GOTHAM'S WHO'S WHO SHOW UP FOR DUBELZ'S SEND-OFF. NOT SURPRISIN'.

OLD CREEP HAD HALF THE TOWN IN HIS POCKET...

MOST OF MOE AN' JOE'S BOYS ARE AT THE WAKE, BUT THEY'LL STILL BE PACKIN'. COUPLE ON GUARD DUTY.

LET 'EM ALL COME IN. MORE THE MERRIER.

HOLD ON...

SUITS ME. MORE OF 'EM I HAVE TO WADE THROUGH ON MY WAY TO THE TWINS, LESS TO WORRY ABOUT LATER.

WHO'S *THAT*?

39

SO FAR HE'S SPOTTED SIX PRIESTS, A JUDGE OR TWO, AND THE CAPTAINS OF THE THIRD, TENTH AND SIXTEENTH PRECINCTS.

TOO MANY LAWYERS AND STREET COPS TO COUNT.

OLD MAN DUBELZ WAS RATHER WELL-CONNECTED...

THIS IS WHAT HE FIGHTS FOR, IS IT? WHY A *THING* FROM *HELL* USES HIM AS A BOLT HOLE?

AH, HE WAS A FINE MAN, BOYS.

HE WAS INDEED, FATHER BUSHMILLS.

A GREAT MAN.

YES, FATHER.

SHEEP. CATTLE. PIGS.

AND HE GETS THAT FEELING, THE WAY HE ALWAYS DOES, THAT TEMPTATION TO TREAT THE WORLD THE WAY IT TREATS HIM...

TO LET IT GO TO HELL.

AND THEN DESTINY TAKES IT CLEAN OUT OF HIS HANDS.

THE WAY IT ALWAYS DOES.

KRASH!

OMIGAWD!

NOW'S AS GOOD
A TIME AS ANY--

KRAKK!

BLAM!
BLAM!
BLAM!

HUH?

BLAM!
BLAM!
BLAM!
BLAM!

WORLD'S WORST
COOK

AAAAAARRGGH!

BLAM!
BLAM!

UNNNGHH--

BLAM! BLAM!

45

48

UUGGHH! AAAAAH! EEIIGHH!

WHAT THE HELL IS *THIS*--?

HOWDY, *HITMAN!* DAMN FINE SHOW! FATSO'S FEELING RATHER--

WHOA!

NOW... PULLING ICE MACHINES ON DEMONS IS A RISKY THING TO DO-- I MUST ADMIT I DO ADMIRE YOUR GUTS!

SO WHY DON'T YOU UNWIND... AND READ THIS DEMON'S MIND...

AND YOU'LL SEE I'M ONLY HERE TO KICK *FAT BUTT!*

HE JERKS UPRIGHT, RIGID --HIS HEAD SHATTERS A CHANDELIER SIX FEET ABOVE --

WHUMPSHH!

GUESS DIRTY HARRY WAS RIGHT.

NO! AAAARRGHH!

now you're in a sticky spot! with your tongue tied in a knot!

YOU'RE DEAD, MONAGHAN!

DEAD! DEAD! DEAD!

BLAM! BLAM! BLAM!

AAAAAHH!

HITMAN

GARTH ENNIS
WRITER

JOHN McCREA
ARTIST

GLEN MURAKAMI
COLORIST

KEN LOPEZ
LETTERER

I GOTTA TELL YOU, WHEN I CAME OUT 'HERE TONIGHT I EXPECTED TO GET RICH QUICK...

BUT THIS, MAN, *THIS* IS BEYOND MY WILDEST DREAMS.

I'LL GET TEN TIMES MORE FOR YOU THAN I EVER WOULDA FOR MONAGHAN, BATFREAK. DON FRANCINI, MOE DUBELZ, BLACK MASK-- ANYONE'VE 'EM'LL PAY TOP WHACK FOR YOU.

SO YOU KNOW WHAT I'M GONNA DO? I'M GONNA PULL THE TRIGGER. THEN I'M GONNA CUT WHAT'S LEFT OF YOUR HEAD OFF.

AN' THEN I'M GONNA MAKE A FEW CALLS AN' SEE WHO'LL PAY THE MOST TO SEE THE BATMAN DEAD--

AN' THEN I'M GONNA OVERNIGHT 'EM YOUR CUTE LITTLE BAT-EARED NOGGIN.

BUT FIRST I'M GONNA STAND HERE AN' MESS WITH YOU A WHILE, 'CUZ THIS IS JUST TOO GOOD A CHANCE TO MISS.

Not now.

Not with my city rotting from a plague without a cure. Not when I've gone without sleep for nearly two days.

I would have better things to do than deal with petty killers--

If I were not the Batman.

WAAAGHH!!

64

BATMAN, DARK KNIGHT OF GOTHAM CITY, THIS IS MARTIN ECKSTEIN, TENTH-RATE ASSASSIN AND COMPLETE SOCIAL INCOMPETENT.

I'M YOUR HOST, TOMMY MONAGHAN-- ALL-AROUND NICE GUY AND SO FAST ON THE TRIGGER YOU WOULDN'T BELIEVE IT...

A.K.A. HITMAN.

HITMAN...?

JUST SOUNDED KINDA SNAPPY, I GUESS. TELLS YOU EVERYTHING YOU NEED TO KNOW.

WHAT YOU NEED TO KNOW IS THAT I AM BUSY TONIGHT. YOU TWO ARE GOING TO JAIL OR TO THE HOSPITAL.

CHOOSE.

DON'T GO GETTIN' HASTY.

LEMME BRING YOU UP TO SPEED ON THE SITUATION HERE...

KACHAK KACHAK

OKAY, YOU KNOW WE GOT THIS PLAGUE GOIN' ON? WHOLE TOWN'S CURFEWED AN' QUARANTINED, NO ONE GETS IN OR OUT?

GET TO THE POINT.

YOU BETTER PIN YOUR BIG EARS BACK OR IT'S GONNA GET A MILLION TIMES WORSE.

"JUST THIS AFTERNOON I'M CHILLIN' WATCHIN' *SUDDEN IMPACT* AN' CLINT'S JUST GETTIN' DOWN TO SOME SERIOUS POLICE BRUTALITY WHEN THE PHONE RINGS AN' IT'S THIS MARINE COLONEL I KNOW..."

"I GOT A FEW CONTACTS FROM MY TIME IN THE CORPS AN' THEY USE ME FOR JOBS NOW AND THEN..."

"... YOU KNOW, WHEN THEY NEED A GUY WHACKED BUT CAN'T MAKE IT TOO OFFICIAL?"

"SO THERE'S THIS PLACE ON LONG ISLAND WHERE THEY DO RESEARCH INTO BIO-WARFARE --AN' IT SEEMS LIKE THEY'VE HAD KIND OF A BREAKOUT..."

NO ENTRY

EXTREME BIOHAZARD

"THEY'VE COME UP WITH A GUY CALLED *THRAX.*"

"NOW, THRAX IS A KIND OF WALKING DISEASE *BOMB.* THEY ENGINEERED HIM SO THEY COULD DROP HIM INTO AN ENEMY CITY, AN' HE'LL JUST WALK AROUND SPREADIN' PNEU-MONIA, EBOLA, THE MUMPS--HELL, WHATEVER THEY DECIDE TO FILL HIM UP WITH.

"YOUR TAX DOLLARS AT WORK, HUH?"

"BUT THRAX AIN'T TOO KEEN ON THAT IDEA. HE BUSTS OUT AN' RUNS LIKE HELL, AN' THEY LOSE CONTACT WITH HIM ON THE OUTSKIRTS OF GOTHAM."

"THE PLACE IS SEALED TIGHT WITH THE PLAGUE LOOSE, SO THEY NEED SOMEONE ALREADY IN TOWN TO CLEAN UP THEIR MESS."

GUESS WHO?

AND THRAX IS *HERE*? SPREADING *MORE* DISEASE?

UH-UH. DOESN'T WORK LIKE THAT. HE'S GOTTA *WANT* TO LET THE STUFF OUT OF HIS PORES.

ALL THRAX WANTS RIGHT NOW IS TO STAY ALIVE.

"PROBLEM IS, HE'S GOT A BUILT-IN DETONATOR HE DOESN'T KNOW ABOUT. HE'S IMMUNE TO HIS OWN POISONS, BUT IF IT LOOKED LIKE HE WAS GONNA GET CAPTURED, HIS BOSSES COULD BLOW HIM TO HELL. MAXIMUM DENIABILITY."

"THEY GOT ALL KINDS OF INFRARED SECURITY STUFF WHERE THEY BUILT HIM. THEY FIGURE IT SET OFF THE DETONATOR WHEN THRAX BROKE OUT."

COUNTDOWN'S STARTED, BATGUY. YOU DON'T LET ME GO, HE'S GONNA *BURST*.

COME ON, MAN, I'M TRYNNA BE NICE ABOUT THIS.

LAST THING I WANNA DO IS BLOW YOU AWAY.

If this is true...

It HAS to be stopped, or Gotham is finished.

But there is NO WAY I will let this murderer collect his pay on MY watch...

AW HELL.

YOU'RE GONNA DO IT THE HARD WAY, AIN'T YOU? I KNOW YOU ARE.

YOU'RE THINKIN', "NO WAY I WILL LET THIS MURDERER COLLECT HIS PAY..."

LUCKY GUESS. ECKSTEIN!

WAH!

LISTEN, YOU GOTTA PUT YOUR GUN ON BATBOY, OKAY?

I ONLY GOT TWO GUNS. I CAN'T COVER YOU AND HIM AT THE SAME TIME. YOU DON'T COVER HIM, HE'S GONNA GET OFF 'CAUSE I GOT MY GUN ON YOU AN' NO ONE'LL BE THERE TO COVER HIM.

BUT IF YOU COVER HIM, THEN I CAN COVER US BOTH 'CAUSE I GOT TWO GUNS. THAT WAY YOU CAN COVER HIM WITHOUT ME GETTIN' AWAY. AN' HE CAN'T SAY SPIT ABOUT IT 'CAUSE HE AIN'T EVEN GOT A GUN.

YOU WITH ME?

ER...

NOBODY would fall for THAT...

69

OH NO?

YOU KIDS PLAY NICE NOW, YOU HEAR?

LISTEN TO ME-- I HAVE TO GO AFTER HIM. IF I CAN GET A SAMPLE OF THRAX'S BLOOD, I *MIGHT* BE ABLE TO DEVELOP AN *ANTIDOTE* TO THE *PLAGUE.*

PUT THE GUN DOWN, ECKSTEIN. MILLIONS COULD DIE IF YOU DON'T.

YOU COULD DIE.

HMMM.

NO, I DON'T THINK SO. I GOT A BETTER IDEA.

I'M SURE.

WHOA!

I KNEW YOU'D LEAD ME STRAIGHT TO HIM-- BUT I DON'T HAVE TIME TO FIGHT.

THRAX'S BLOOD COULD SAVE THIS CITY, MONAGHAN. I NEED IT *NOW*, WHILE HE STILL BREATHES.

YOU AIN'T GOT TIME FOR THAT, BATMAN. CLOCK'S TICKIN', REMEMBER?

YOU GOTTA GET OUTTA MY WAY OR THE WHOLE CITY'S A FREAKIN' *HOT ZONE*--

NO.

I WILL NOT LET YOU EARN BLOOD MONEY OFF THIS CREATURE'S LIFE.

I WILL NOT LET YOU KILL THIS MAN.

FOR CRYIN' OUT LOUD, BATMAN! *LOOK AT HIM!*

LOOK! HE'S DEAD *NOW* ! HIS FREAKIN' POX-TIMER'S KILLED HIM! *HE'S GONNA BLOW NO MATTER WHAT YOU DO!*

SEE THIS? WHITE PHOSPHORUS. THIS'LL BURN HIM AN' HIS LOUSY DISEASES UP LIKE THEY WERE NEVER THERE--

BUT YOU GOTTA GET OUTTA MY WAY!

DO IT.

SORE LOSER.

74

JUST RIGHT NOW THOUGH, I AIN'T GETTING A RED CENT FOR THESE IDIOTS--

'CAUSE BELIEVE IT OR NOT, THIS IS SELF-DEFENSE.

CUT HIM IN HALF!

TWO YEARS BACK I GOT ON THE WRONG SIDE OF ONE OF GOTHAM CITY'S NASTIER MOB BOSSES, AND EVERY SO OFTEN HE FEELS THE NEED TO REMIND ME.

THE KIND OF HIRED SCUM HE SENDS AIN'T MUCH MORE THAN A DISTRACTION--

BUT I MEAN, ALL I WANT IS POKER NIGHT AT NOONAN'S-- AND WHAT I GET IS SHOT AT, CHASED INTO THIS LOUSY WAREHOUSE AND SHOT AT EVEN MORE--

OH GOD--

WHO NEEDS IT?

78

BA KOOM!

BEING GOOD LITTLE KILLERS, EINSTEIN AND CO. HAVE A MAN OUT BACK WHO'S GONNA BUST IN FIRING ABOUT TWO SECONDS FROM NOW.

HOW DO I KNOW THIS?

I'VE GOT SUPERPOWERS.

DIE, YOU--!

PICKED 'EM UP IN CIRCUMSTANCES TOO INSANE TO GO INTO RIGHT NOW.

LET'S JUST SAY THE X-RAY VISION'S GOOD, BUT THE TELEPATHY...

OH GOD OH GOD OH LORD HELP ME PLEASE--BEG HIM BEG HIM TO LET ME GO BEG BEG--

PLEATH! PLEATH LEHMUH GUH!

BEG! BEG! BEG!

(AND THEN WASTE HIM)

...I LOVE THE TELEPATHY.

BLAM

SHOOM!

SHADOW-FORCE!

DAMMIT--!

79

SURRENDER, MONAGHAN! YOU DON'T STAND A CHANCE AGAINST *SHADOW-FORCE!*

OH, GREAT.

MONAGHAN! COME ON OUT!

IT'S WAY TOO EASY TO GET SUPERPOWERS THESE DAYS--HELL, I SHOULD KNOW.

YOU SEE THESE GUYS EVERY WEEK ON T.V.: SOMEONE FALLS INTO A REACTOR OR FINDS OUT HIS DAD WAS HALF-DEMON OR WHATEVER. YOU KNOW THE ROUTINE.

'CEPT NOW IT LOOKS LIKE THIS MOBSTER I GOT MAD AT ME SAVED UP AND HIRED A *TEAM* OF 'EM.

RIGHT! YOU ASKED FOR IT!

CHEAP SUPERVILLAINS. I DUNNO.

READY, *TWILIGHT!*

READY, *DARKSTORM!*

BUT I GOTTA ADMIT:

READY, *MINK!*

RRRRR!

IF IT WASN'T FOR THEM, I'D BE OUT'VE A JOB.

80

COCKATOO!

READY!

LIKE I WAS SAYING, I KILL PEOPLE FOR MONEY.

PEOPLE LIKE THIS.

PANZER!

READY!

REGULAR HITMEN KILL REGULAR PEOPLE. I AIN'T REGULAR HITMEN.

I TAKE THE WEIRD JOBS...

IRONBOLT!

READY!

GET MUGGED BY A CYBORG? CALL ME. DARKSEID KIDNAP MOM? CALL ME. SWAMP THINGY SCARE YOUR KIDS? CALL ME. POSSESSED BY ETRIGAN AND DON'T KNOW ANY EXORCISTS? CALL ME.

SHADOW-FORCE GO!!

NUMBER ONE IN A FIELD OF ONE. SUPERPOWERED, SUPERNATURAL OR JUST SUPER-FREAKIN' ANNOYING:

I DO 'EM ALL.

BLAM BLAM BLAM BLAM BLAM BLAM

BLAM BLAM BLAM BLAM BLAM

BLAM BLAM BLAM BLAM BLAM

BLAM BLAM BLAM BLAM

IF ANYBODY'S NOT DEAD, NOW WOULD BE A GOOD TIME TO SAY.

LEMME TELL YOU WHAT "RESERVOIR DOGS" IS REALLY ABOUT...

NOONAN'S

IT'S ALL ABOUT GUYS WHO GOT HIT WHEN THEY WERE KIDS. A BEATEN CHILD BECOMES A PSYCHOTIC ARMED ROBBER, GET ME?

THE ENTIRE THING, IT'S A METAPHOR FOR CHILD ABUSE--

NO IT AIN'T.

IT'S ABOUT TRUST AN' HONOR AN' FRIENDSHIP. LIKE THAT.

WHERE THE HELL IS TOMMY?

HEY, SEAN. PAT. RINGO.

WHAT, I DON'T COUNT, OR SOMETHING?

NOPE.

Panel 1:

OH, THAT'S NICE. I LIKE THAT.

HEY, HACKEN? HOW DO YOU SPELL "EDUCATIONALLY SUB-NORMAL"?

Panel 2:

HOW DO YOU SPELL "HIDING BEHIND YOUR BUDDY MONAGHAN," YOU LITTLE BASTARD?

CAN WE PLAY POKER?

Panel 3:

WEDNESDAY NIGHT IS POKER NIGHT. YOU PROBABLY FIGURE I SKIN THESE GUYS EVERY TIME, WHAT WITH THE X-RAY EYES AND THE MIND-READING, BUT NO: I GOT *ETHICS.*

AND WITHOUT ETHICS, WHERE ARE YOU?

IT'S PRETTY MUCH A BULL SESSION WITH CARDS AND BEER. AFFAIRS OF STATE, FASHION, RELATIONSHIPS, THE MEDIA: NOTHING ESCAPES OUR RUTHLESS SCRUTINY. SEAN'S TALKING ABOUT INVITING OPRAH.

I SAY THAT'S SWELL, AS LONG AS OPRAH GETS HERSELF A MAGNUM AN' A BODYCOUNT...

'CAUSE POKER NIGHT IS *HITMEN ONLY.*

SEE YOU AN' RAISE, RINGO. YOU GUYS WATCH THE GAME MONDAY NIGHT?

IT SUCKED.

GUESS SOMEONE HAD HIS MONEY ON GOTHAM AGAIN...

WHEN WILL I EVER LEARN?

Panel 4:

SEAN OWNS THE PLACE. HE USED TO WHACK GUYS IN THE FIFTIES. NOW HE SAYS US KIDS HAVE IT EASY, IN HIS DAY A KILLER *WORKED* FOR HIS MONEY, BLAH BLAH BLAH.

HE'S KINDA LIKE A FATHER TO ME, I GUESS. I MEAN, I DUNNO WHAT A FATHER'S SUPPOSED TO BE LIKE. I NEVER KNEW MINE.

Panel 5:

I FOLD. HEY, YOU GUYS HEAR THE ONE ABOUT SUPERMAN, WONDER WOMAN AN' MISTER INVISIBLE?

PAT AIN'T EXACTLY A HITMAN, BUT HE'S SEAN'S NEPHEW AN' A GOOD FRIEND OF MINE.

HE LETS HIS MOUTH GET HIM INTO TROUBLE WITHOUT FIGURING A WAY OUT FIRST. KIND OF LIKE BUGS BUNNY, ONLY NOT AS TOUGH.

84

THERE IS NOT A MAN OR WOMAN ON THE PLANET WHO HAS NOT HEARD THAT JOKE, PAT.

RAISE.

RINGO, NOW, RINGO IS A KILLER WITH *STYLE*. THOSE ICE-BLUE EYES OF HIS NEVER MISS A TRICK. HE'S POLITE, HE'S THOUGHTFUL, HE'S KIND TO SMALL ANIMALS AND CHILDREN AND HE'S KILLED MAYBE TWO HUNDRED GUYS ON HIS WAY UP FROM NEW YORK'S CHINATOWN.

WE COME OUT ABOUT EVEN AT CARDS, ME AN' RINGO. I FIGURE THAT AIN'T THE ONLY THING WE'RE EVEN AT, BUT I AIN'T IN ANY HURRY TO FIND OUT.

HACKEN--

EEERRRP WHO'S MISTER INVISIBLE?

HACKEN'S A CLASS ACT.

HE'S THAT GUY IN THE JUSTICE CLUB. YOU KNOW, WITH THE GAS MASK.

JUSTICE LEAGUE, BUTTWIPE. AIN'T NO JUSTICE CLUB.

SURE THERE IS. THE OLD GUYS, ONE OF 'EM'S GOT THE SOUP BOWL ON HIS HEAD.

I FOLD. HE MEANS JUSTICE *SOCIETY*.

YOU EVER WONDER HOW MUCH PREPARATION H THOSE GUYS GO THROUGH?

OKAY, I CALL. ANYWAY, WHY DOES HE HAVE A GAS MASK?

HE NEEDS IT FOR WHEN HE SHOOTS DUST AT PEOPLE. MAKES 'EM INVISIBLE... OR AM I THINKIN' OF SOMEONE ELSE?

WHOA, HACKEN! TWO KINGS! MAVERICK'S IN THE HOUSE!

IF I GET ONE MORE CRACK OUT OF YOU, YOU~

I STAY ONE HAND AHEAD OF RINGO FOR THE REST OF THE NIGHT, WHICH IS GOOD BECAUSE I BLEW A THOUSAND BUCKS ON THE LOUSY BALLGAME. HAPPENS TO ME A LOT, OR I'D BE ON A BEACH IN RIO RIGHT NOW.

CENTS ONLY

WE HAVE BODDIES IN THE CELLAR

WINNER BUYS THE BEER.

THANKS. LISTEN, STAY AWAY FROM THE BOOKIES, OKAY? YOU PICK WINNERS LIKE HACKEN PICKS UP BROADS...

SOMEDAY... I'LL... I'LL SHOW 'EM ALL...

I'LL MAKE A DEAL WITH YOU: YOU QUIT SMOKIN' THOSE STINKIN' FREAKIN' CIGARS AN' MAYBE I'LL THINK ABOUT IT.

NO DEAL.

SEE YOU, RINGO. PAT, I'LL SEE YOU TOMORROW FOR THAT THING, OKAY?

'KAY.

WHY DOES HE NEVER TAKE HIS SHADES OFF, DO YOU SUPPOSE?

'CAUSE HIS EYES ARE--

DO YOU' THINK IT HAS ANYTHING TO DO WITH HIM BEING THE ONLY KILLER TO TAKE ON METAHUMAN CONTRACTS?

I MEAN, I DUNNO. WHO CAN TELL? MAYBE HE JUST LIKES 'EM ON.

DOUBT IT. I FIGURE HE JUST SAW A GAP IN THE MARKET, YOU KNOW? NO ONE ELSE WAS DOIN' THAT KINDA WORK.'

...COULDA BEEN A CONTENDER...

MM. OF COURSE, THE PROBLEM WITH THAT KIND OF WORK IS...

IT'S BOUND TO BRING ITS OWN KIND OF HEAT.

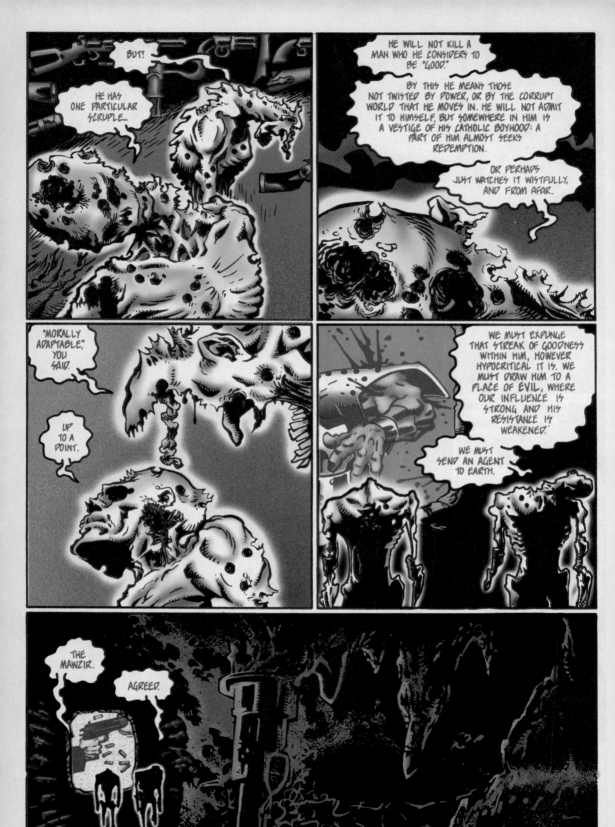

BUT!

HE HAS ONE PARTICULAR SCRUPLE...

HE WILL NOT KILL A MAN WHO HE CONSIDERS TO BE "GOOD."

BY THIS HE MEANS THOSE NOT TWISTED BY POWER, OR BY THE CORRUPT WORLD THAT HE MOVES IN. HE WILL NOT ADMIT IT TO HIMSELF, BUT SOMEWHERE IN HIM IS A VESTIGE OF HIS CATHOLIC BOYHOOD: A PART OF HIM ALMOST SEEKS REDEMPTION.

OR PERHAPS JUST WATCHES IT WISTFULLY, AND FROM AFAR.

"MORALLY ADAPTABLE," YOU SAID.

UP TO A POINT.

WE MUST EXPUNGE THAT STREAK OF GOODNESS WITHIN HIM, HOWEVER HYPOCRITICAL IT IS. WE MUST DRAW HIM TO A PLACE OF EVIL, WHERE OUR INFLUENCE IS STRONG AND HIS RESISTANCE IS WEAKENED."

WE MUST SEND AN AGENT TO EARTH.

THE MAWZIR.

AGREED.

88

89

♪ OH, THE TORN-UP TICKET STUBS FROM ♪ A HUNDRED THOUSAND MUGS... NOW WASHED AWAY LIKE DEAD DREAMS IN THE RAIN... ♪

YOU KNOW, IF YOU GOT YOURSELF A REVOLVER WE WOULDN'T HAVE TO GO THROUGH ALL THAT CRAP WORRYING ABOUT FINGERPRINTS ON THE SHELL CASES...

SURE, THEN I COULD POP OFF SIX SHOTS AND STAND THERE LOOKING STUPID. ANYWAY, WHAT'RE YOU BITCHING ABOUT? I PAY YOU FOR YOUR TIME, DON'T I?

YOU BOUGHT ME A CASE OF BEER. IT AIN'T QUITE THE SAME THING.

AND YOU'LL PROBABLY DRINK HALF OF IT ON ME...

IT AIN'T JUST BEER, IT'S SIERRA NEVADA--

OH!

OOF--

... OH, I'M SORRY... er...

S'OKAY. MY FAULT.

LET ME, um, GET YOUR...

HEY, IT'S HEAVY!

YEAH, IT'S FULL OF BULLETS.

BULLETS?

I'M AN ASSASSIN.

YOU GOTTA BE OUTTA YOUR MIND. WHAT IF SHE'D BELIEVED YOU?

HANGIN' AROUND WITH YOU'S GETTIN' TO BE BAD FOR MY HEART, YOU KNOW THAT?

RELAX. I GOT HER PHONE NUMBER, DIDN'T I?

AN' I DIDN'T EVEN HAVE TO LIE.

YOU HATE INDIAN. I NEVER SEEN YOU EAT INDIAN IN YOUR LIFE.

YEAH, BUT SHE LOVES IT. AN' I GOT A FEELIN' SHE'LL BE WORTH IT.

WORTH THE YELLOW RICE...THE POPADOMS...THE ENDLESS CURRY...

RING RING RING

YEAH? OH, RIGHT.

YEAH, YOU'RE IN LUCK. HE'S HERE.

McWILLIAMS.

Ah-ha.

HEY, GERRY. YEAH. YEAH, BUT I KEEP MY STUFF HERE AT PAT'S.

YOU DO, huh? HOW JUICY IS JUICY?

I'LL BE THERE.

HE GOT WORK FOR YOU? WHO'S THE HIT ON?

COULDN'T SAY ON THE PHONE. BUT, uh, WHOEVER IT IS...

THEY'RE WORTH A MILLION BUCKS.

WELL... WELL...

WHAT I COULD DO WITH A MILLION BUCKS, huh? MOVE OUT OF TOWN TO START WITH...

MANHATTAN, MAYBE. IT'S KINDA LIKE GOTHAM, BUT WITH SUNLIGHT...

WHOA, BOY! REMEMBER THE LAST TIME YOU GOT PROMISED A MILLION DOLLARS? THAT JASON BLOOD JERK?

YOU DIDN'T GET TO SEE A CENT!

♪ START SPREADIN' THE NEWS... I'M LEAVIN' TODAY... ♪

WHAT'S THE USE?

93

YOU GOTTA BE KIDDING ...!

Uh-uh. GUY GOT IN TOUCH WITH ME THROUGH FRANCINI'S PEOPLE. THINK HE'S PALS WITH THE DON.

ANYWAY, LAST TIME THIS WACKO GOT LOOSE HE SMILE-GASSED A KINDERGARTEN IN THE HEIGHTS. ONE OF THE KIDS WAS THIS RICH GUY'S SON, AN' I GUESS HE WAS KINDA UPSET TO HEAR THAT LITTLE JIMMY CHOKED TO DEATH ON HIS OWN PUKE...

HENCE THE MILLION-DOLLAR HIT.

I DUNNO, GERRY. IT AIN'T WHAT I WAS EXPECTING AT ALL.

SO WHAT WERE YOU EXPECTING?

GOOD POINT.

ASK ME, IT'S A PRETTY EASY JOB. AIN'T LIKE THE BASTARD'S HARD TO FIND, AND SECURITY AT ARKHAM MUST BE THE PITS OR THESE PSYCHOS WOULDN'T KEEP GETTIN' OUT.

C'MON, WHAT D'YOU SAY?

YOU'VE TALKED ME INTO IT.

ATTABOY. I'LL CALL THE GUY NOW. MONEY'S YOURS ON COMPLETION.

YOU WANT THE PHOTO?

GEE, MAYBE I SHOULD. I MIGHT FORGET WHAT HE LOOKS LIKE.

94

Hmm.

NO TONGUES.

WELL, THANK YOU FOR DINNER. I REALLY ENJOYED IT.

THAT'S GOOD, 'CAUSE MINE TASTED LIKE DOG CRAP AND SOAP.

MY PLEASURE.

YOU KNOW SOMETHING?

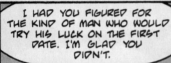

I HAD YOU FIGURED FOR THE KIND OF MAN WHO WOULD TRY HIS LUCK ON THE FIRST DATE. I'M GLAD YOU DIDN'T.

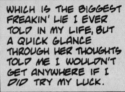

WHICH IS THE BIGGEST FREAKIN' LIE I EVER TOLD IN MY LIFE, BUT A QUICK GLANCE THROUGH HER THOUGHTS TOLD ME I WOULDN'T GET ANYWHERE IF I DID TRY MY LUCK.

NOT MY STYLE.

AND I FIGURE SHE'LL BE WORTH THE WAIT.

A GENTLEMAN. THANK YOU.

CALL ME, OKAY?

YOU BET. G'NIGHT.

♪ JUST AN OLD- ♪ FASHIONED GIRL, WITH AN OLD-FASHIONED-- ♪

BATARANG.

BATARANG?

SHONK!

A RAGE IN ARKHAM

PART TWO

garth **ENNIS** writer · john **McCREA** artist · willie **SCHUBERT** letterer · carla **FEENY** colorist · heroic **AGE** color seps. · peter **TOMASI** asst. editor · dan **RASPLER** editor · **HITMAN** created by **ENNIS** & **McCREA**

WELL, THIS IS GREAT...

DITKO POUR HOMME

VISIT STEVES DRAWING EMPORIUM OUR SPECIALITY

YOU HUNGRY?

MM.

RIGHT. WE DUMP THE PUNK FIRST, THEN WE HIT BUCKETBURGER. WE GET TWO FIVE-POUNDERS WITH BACONCHEESE DOUBLESLUDGE AN' A SIX OF BUD. AN' WE GO WATCH THE GANGBANGERS IN THE PROJECTS.

BETTER'N THE GAME.

OKAY, BUT MAKE IT BUD LITE.

NO WAY IN HELL AM I GOING TO THE JOINT TO GET A SHIV BETWEEN MY RIBS, NOT WITH A MILLION CASH AN' ANOTHER DATE WITH WENDY ON THE CARDS...

LET'S SEE IF THESE TWO CLOWNS CAN HELP:

Ah-HAAA...!

YOU TWO BEEN PARTNERS A WHILE NOW, huh?

SHUT IT, BUTTWIPE.

SO BUCK... WHAT WOULD YOU SAY IF I TOLD YOU ANDY HERE HAD A THING GOING WITH YOUR OLD LADY?

WWHAAT?

107

BATMAN, HUH? YOU GET HIS AUTOGRAPH?

MAYBE NEXT TIME.

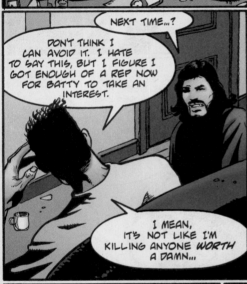

NEXT TIME...?

DON'T THINK I CAN AVOID IT. I HATE TO SAY THIS, BUT I FIGURE I GOT ENOUGH OF A REP NOW FOR BATTY TO TAKE AN INTEREST.

I MEAN, IT'S NOT LIKE I'M KILLING ANYONE WORTH A DAMN...

ALL LIFE IS SACRED, THOMAS. EVEN THE JOKER WAS ONCE SOME MOTHER'S SON.

HE'S A MOTHERLOVIN' BOMB WAITIN' TO GO OFF, IS WHAT HE IS. A SENSIBLE MAN WOULDA BUST A CAP IN HIM YEARS AGO.

BUT OH NO, NOT BATBOY...

I GUESS YOU'D BETTER GET USED TO IT.

HUH?

WELL, YOU'RE GONNA BE MEETIN' A LOT MORE SUPERGUYS NOW YOU GOT YOUR POWERS, AIN'T YOU? PROBABLY BE JOININ' THE JUSTICE LEAGUE SOON.

SAY, LISTEN, CAN I BE YOUR KID SIDE-KICK?

THE FINGER. ORIGINAL.

BATS IS JUST ONE MORE REASON TO LEAVE TOWN AFTER THE ARKHAM HIT--

YOU'RE STILL GOIN' THROUGH WITH IT?!

MILLION BUCKS.

MILLION-TO-ONE CHANCE YOU'LL GET AWAY WITH IT! YOU GOTTA BE KIDDIN' ME, TOMMY--

Uh-uh.

WHACKIN' GUYS PAYS OKAY, BUT IT AIN'T GOT MUCH CAREER PROSPECTS EXCEPT FOR TWO IN THE BACK OF THE HEAD SOME DAY YOU AIN'T LOOKIN'...

SEAN RETIRED WITHOUT GETTIN' HIT--

YEAH, FLAT BROKE. NO DISRESPECT TO SEAN, I LOVE THE OLD GUY--BUT I DON'T WANNA END MY DAYS TENDIN' BAR IN A FREAKIN' GOTHAM SLUM.

I NEED THAT MILLION TO MOVE TO NEW YORK, GET A PLACE IN BROOKLYN. DRINK BEER, EAT PIZZA, WATCH THE SUN SET OVER THE SKYLINE.

IT'S SOMETHIN' TO SEE, PAT. YOU SEE THE SUN GO DOWN IN GOTHAM, IT'S LIKE IT'S FALLIN' INTO HELL. NOT THERE, THOUGH.

NOT THERE.

...I'D MISS YOU.

SO COME WITH ME.

LOCK UP YOUR DAUGHTERS, MANHATTAN.

112

113

SO WHEN I DO GO IN, THEY FIGURE THEY'RE GOOD AN' READY FOR ME:

THEY GOT SNIPERS...

CAMERAS...

THEY GOT TWO DOZEN COPS ALL LOADED FOR BEAR...

INFRARED TRIP-BEAMS EVERYWHERE...

AND ROVER.

HELL, EVERYONE'S MADE THE PARTY--

AND I CAN SEE 'EM ALL.

I, uh... I THINK IT'S GOIN' DOWN, CHARLIE...

HOW SO?

'CAUSE THE GUY'S STANDIN' HERE WITH A GUN IN MY EAR.

115

116

HUHNNNHGOD THE PAIN--

I NEARLY FORGOT, THERE'S A MESSAGE TO GO WITH IT:

LIAM DAWSON SAYS, "NOTHING PERSONAL, HATTER--BUT NEXT TIME I SELL YOU GUNS, YOU GOTTA REMEMBER TO PAY."

GOT THAT?

GET A DOLTOR! PLEASE GET A DOCTOR!

I'M BEGGING YOU!

I FIGURE THEY'LL HAVE A COP OR TWO RIGHT AT THE JOKER'S CELL-ROW...

YEP.

STUN GRENADE AGAIN--HEY, WHAT DO YOU TAKE ME FOR?

TEN-FIVER, WE GOT--

SSSSSSS

PLNT,

PLUNK!

--TROUBLE N--KRZZKKTT!

THE LAST ROW OF CELLS--

THE *LAST ROW OF CELLS* IS WHERE THEY KEEP THE *REAL SCUM*, THE ONES THAT OUGHTA BE LOCKED AWAY IN THE DARK FOREVER--HELL, THEY OUGHTA BEEN *STRANGLED AT BIRTH.*

AND YEAH, I ADMIT IT.

I'M SPOOKED.

FHSSHSSHSSS

I SAW THE MOVIE, THANKS.

I'M KINDA TEMPTED TO DO 'EM ALL, YOU KNOW THAT? I MEAN, WHAT THE HELL ELSE SHOULD A SANE MAN--

A RAGE IN ARKHAM

PART THREE

garth ENNIS	john McCREA	willie SCHUBERT	carla FEENY	heroic AGE	peter TOMASI	dan RASPLER	HITMAN created by ENNIS & McCREA
writer	artist	letterer	colorist	color seps.	asst. editor	editor	

126

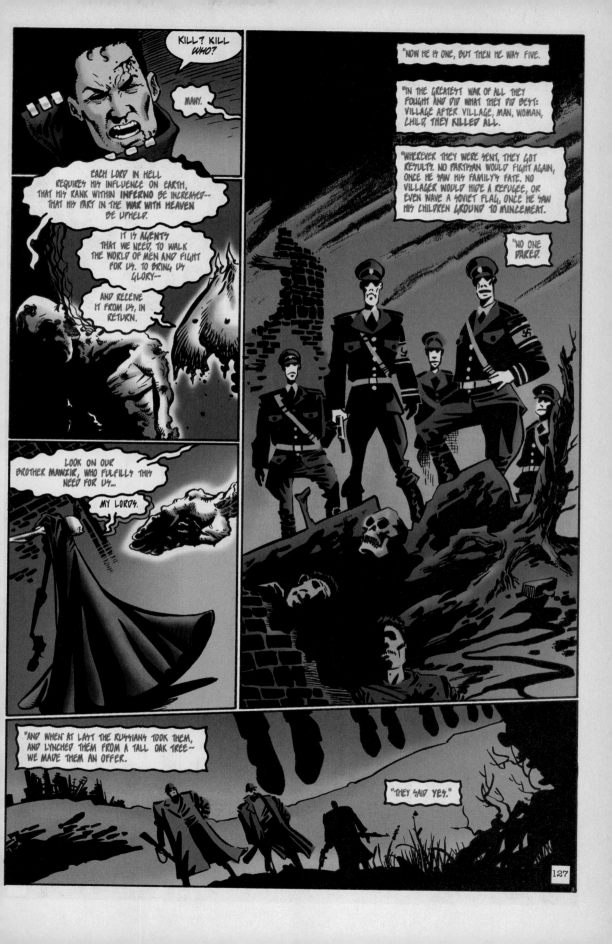

KILL? KILL WHO?

MANY.

EACH LORD IN HELL REQUIRES HIS INFLUENCE ON EARTH, THAT HIS RANK WITHIN **INFERNO** BE INCREASED-- THAT HIS PART IN THE WAR WITH HEAVEN BE UPHELD.

IT IS AGENTS THAT WE NEED, TO WALK THE WORLD OF MEN AND FIGHT FOR US, TO BRING US GLORY--

AND RECEIVE IT FROM US, IN RETURN.

LOOK ON OUR BROTHER MAWZIR, WHO FULFILLS THIS NEED FOR US...

MY LORDS.

"NOW HE IS ONE, BUT THEN HE WAS FIVE.

"IN THE GREATEST WAR OF ALL THEY FOUGHT AND DID WHAT THEY DID BEST: VILLAGE AFTER VILLAGE, MAN, WOMAN, CHILD, THEY KILLED ALL.

"WHEREVER THEY WERE SENT, THEY GOT RESULTS. NO PARTISAN WOULD FIGHT AGAIN, ONCE HE SAW HIS FAMILY'S FATE. NO VILLAGER WOULD HIDE A REFUGEE, OR EVEN WAVE A SOVIET FLAG, ONCE HE SAW HIS CHILDREN GROUND TO MINCEMEAT.

"NO ONE DARED.

"AND WHEN AT LAST THE RUSSIANS TOOK THEM, AND LYNCHED THEM FROM A TALL OAK TREE— WE MADE THEM AN OFFER.

"THEY SAID YES."

127

FOOOM!!

STUN-GRENADES'LL ONLY GET YOU SO FAR. THAT'S WHY I RECOMMEND A GOOD FRAG--

DAMMIT, THIS *HURTS!*

MONAGHAN, YOU--

CROC WAS *WATCHING THAT!!*

WOOMP! WOOMP!

SSSSLUMM...!

130

HE'S HIT AN ARTERY! HELP ME, BAT-SAMARITAN!

OH NO.

ROLL, YOU IDIOT-- ROLL AND PRAY--

BADAM!

BADAM!

BADAM!

BADAM BADAM BADAM

POP POP

BADAM BADAM BADAM

YOU'RE ALL UNDER-- OH HELL--

HEL-LO...

YOU BASTARD, MONAGHAN--

POP

YOU'RE FINISHED.

IN THAT CASE, I DEMAND PROTECTIVE CUSTODY--

RRRRAAAARRGHHH!

I WON'T TELL ANYONE IF YOU WON'T! HAHAHAHAHA!

KEEP IT UP, JOKER. YOU'RE KILLING ME.

135

THEN IT ALL GOES INTO SLO-MO...

AND THE BASTARD TURNS ON ME...

SCARED FOR THE FIRST TIME, AND HE'S *FAST* ALL RIGHT...

BUT LEMME TELL YOU: YOU PUT A GUN IN *MY* HAND--

AND *NOBODY'S* FASTER.

BADAM! BADAM! BADAM!

AAAAAAAAAAAAHHH!!

WELL, WELL, WELL.

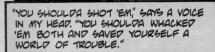

"YOU SHOULDA SHOT 'EM," SAYS A VOICE IN MY HEAD. "YOU SHOULDA WHACKED 'EM BOTH AND SAVED YOURSELF A WORLD OF TROUBLE."

BUT IT'S A SAD, STUPID LITTLE VOICE, AND THE HIGHER THE SUN COMES UP AND THE MORE NIGHT TURNS INTO DAY--

THE QUIETER IT GETS.

SO I NEVER GOT MY MILLION BUCKS. ALL I GOT WAS DAMN NEAR KILLED AND SOME VERY BAD PEOPLE GOOD AN' PISSED AT ME.

BUT WHAT THE HELL: MY ASS IS STILL INTACT.

FIGURE I'LL GO HOME, GET SOME SLEEP, CALL PAT AN' HAVE A DRINK WITH HIM AN' SEAN...

...AN' THEN I'LL GO CHECK OUT THE ONE GOOD THING I DO HAVE:

THE SECOND DATE WITH WENDY.

END